What Would You Get?

By Pamela Chanko

ISBN: 978-1-338-88866-9

Editor: Liza Charlesworth
Art Director: Tannaz Fassihi; Designer: Tanya Chernyak
Photos ©: 3: ultura Creative RF/Alamy Stock Photo; 5: Randy Faris/Getty Images; 8: Cavan Images/Getty Images. All other photos © Shutterstock.com.

1 2 3 4 5 6 7 8 9 10   68   31 30 29 28 27 26 25 24 23
Printed in Jiaxing, China. First printing, January 2023.

SCHOLASTIC INC.

This dog is friendly.
Would you get this pet?
Maybe!

This cat is sleepy.
Would you get this pet?
Maybe!

This bunny is soft and cuddly.
Would you get this pet?
Maybe!

This fish is orange.
Would you get this pet?
Maybe!

This bird is able to talk.
Would you get this pet?
Maybe!

This turtle is very tiny.
Would you get this pet?
Maybe!

This elephant is HUGE!
Would you get this pet?
Maybe...not!